The Van

Written by Caroline Harris
Illustrated by Neil Sutherland, Blue-Zoo and Tony Trimmer

It is a BIG hill!

Let me help!

V can not run up the hill.

v-a-n, van!
It is a van!

r-e-d, red!
It is a red van!

But the van will not go.

vvv-vvv!

o-n, on!

The van revs up.

The van begins to go!

J is next to A and M.
j-**a**-**m**, jam!

The van gets stuck in a jam!

j-a-m, jam!
It is a picnic!